DISCIPLESHIP
TRACK
STUDY GUIDE

BASED ON THE BOOK

Spiritual Multiplication
in the Real World

MULTIPLICATION
PRESS

This study guide is based on the book *Spiritual Multiplication in the Real World* by Bob McNabb.

spiritualmultiplication.org

Spiritual Multiplication in the Real World: Missional Community Study Guide

Copyright © 2013 Robert C. McNabb

Second Printing

ISBN 978-1-942374-01-5

CONTENTS

WEEK ONE
Introduction Meeting
7

WEEK TWO
Chapter 1: Stars and Sand
Chapter 2: Maybe Someone Else
11

WEEK THREE
Chapter 3: Trouble in Multiplication Paradise
Chapter 4: Soil
23

WEEK FOUR
Chapter 5: Essential Elements
35

WEEK 5
Chapter 6: Gone Fishing
47

WEEK SIX
Chapter 7: Parenthood
59

WEEK SEVEN
Chapter 8: Learning to Fly
71

WEEK EIGHT
Chapter 9: The Lost Aspect of Disciple-Making
83

WEEK NINE
Chapter 10: You Can!
95

WEEK TEN
Chapter 11: From Vision to Reality
107

APPENDIX
117

WHO SHOULD USE THIS STUDY GUIDE?

- Groups of six to twelve believers who are established in their walk with the Lord and are meaningfully connected to a House Church.

- Disciples who are ready to enter into the adventure of team evangelism and disciple-making

- People who are able to fulfill the requirements of the Team Covenant (next page)

WHAT ARE SOME OF THE MAJOR LEARNING OBJECTIVES OF THIS STUDY?

Participants will gain the following:

- A conviction for disciple-making efforts to be done in the context of a disciple-making team and movement as well as knowledge of the essential elements of a movement

- An understanding of the evangelism process and a commitment to practice those steps together with fellow teammates as part of a team evangelistic effort

- An overview of the disciple-making process and an understanding of how to move disciples from new birth to maturity to reproduction

HOW IS THIS STUDY GUIDE DIFFERENT FROM OTHER D-TRACK MATERIALS?

Most D-Track materials focus on knowledge acquisition. Their primary focus is to learn. This study guide is different. The focus is on doing and building habits. As you build these habits, you will learn, and you will keep learning long after you finish these materials. The habits that you will work together to establish are:

- Daily Time with God (self-feeding on his Word)
- Evangelism
- Prayer for the Lost
- Scripture Memory
- Obedience
- Teamwork

INTRODUCTION

WHAT ARE HOUSE CHURCHES?

Seven Mile Road is a congregation of House Churches—small groups of people cultivating relationships with God, one another, and the community. These groups are designed to meet at the intersection of Word and Prayer, Meal, and Mission. House Church is the primary way to connect with others at Seven Mile Road and engage our city.

HOW WILL THE *SPIRITUAL MULTIPLICATION D-TRACK* EQUIP HOUSE CHURCHES?

The mission of Seven Mile Road is to embody and declare God's redemptive story to every Houstonian. As a participant in this D-Track, you will be driven into deep times of fellowship, prayer, bible study, and accountability as you aim to fulfill this mission and saturate the city of Houston with effective disciple-makers. As you learn and grow in your understanding of making disciple-makers, our prayer is that you would implement what you are learning with your House Church each week. You will have the unique opportunity to help equip the members of your House Church to make disciples of all nations. This D-Track is inviting you to help cultivate further relationships with God, one another, and the lost men, women, and children in our city.

DISCIPLESHIP TRACK COVENANT

As a participant in this D-Track, I promise to do the following to the very best of my ability:

1. Attend no fewer than 9 of the Spiritual Multiplication Team Meetings on Sundays from 10:45 AM to 1:15 PM.

2. Honestly and prayerfully answer a few simple questions with the members of my huddle each week.

3. Spend time reaching out to the lost with my huddle each week.

4. Pray for 5 non-Christians daily throughout the duration of the experience.

5. Attend my House Church each week.

6. Attend the Seven Mile Road Prayer Meeting each month (Note: on the first weeks of the month, there is no Team Meeting, Huddle, or House Church to encourage urgent, corporate, unified prayer).

I will strive, by the grace of God, to meet the above commitments.

Signed _____ Date _____ / _____ / _____

WEEKLY 3-2-1

3 HOURS with Jesus

Everything begins with God. The foundation of a healthy personal ministry must be our own relationship with Christ. Therefore, commit to communing with him through prayer, worship, and reading his Word at least three hours a week.

2 HOURS with the lost

In order to reap, we must sow the seed of the gospel. We will spend at least two hours a week finding lost people, generating interest in Jesus, sharing the gospel, and Lord willing, helping them decide to follow Christ. Jesus sent his disciples two-by-two. In the same way, we want to go out two-by-two with other people on our team. We may not share the gospel every time, but we will always do something evangelistic, like meeting new people, sharing our testimonies, praying for people's needs, or inviting them to experience our community.

1 HOUR with each other in prayer

Jesus informs us that the key to the harvest is prayer. To see people enter into the Kingdom of God, we must become a people dedicated to prayer both privately and corporately. As a community, we will dedicate at least one hour of corporate prayer for the lost and the nations each week.

WEEKLY TEAM MEETINGS

When it comes to spiritual multiplication, what happens all week long is more important than what happens in a once-a-week meeting. That's why we call our meetings "Team Meetings." They're simply an opportunity to pause once a week and report on what God has been doing in the last six days, pray and encourage one another, plan our next week of ministry, and discuss the week's reading assignments. The components of each meeting are explained below.

WELCOME || 15 minutes

The Welcome portion will provide an opportunity to learn about the others in our community. Each week, we will have a different icebreaker question to discuss.

WITNESS || 10 minutes

The Witness time is an opportunity to share about what God did the previous week in our personal lives or in the lives of our family and friends. (Testimonies of what happened with our lost friends will occur during the Works section.) Be sure to write down a few notes in your workbook so you can look back and remember what God has done.

WORSHIP || 10 minutes

The Worship time is for our group to pray, sing, talk, or praise God in any other way that seems fitting to worship him for who he is and what he has done.

WORKS || 25 minutes

The Works time is for our group to share about what God is doing among our lost friends and plan for the next week's ministry.

Each week, we will write names of our lost friends somewhere that's visible for everyone to see. Names should only be added once you have a person's phone number and are likely to see them again. We will underline names of friends we are studying the Bible with and put a cross next to any people who start following Christ.

We will also start adding some of these names to our FISHing charts (p. 118) as we begin to share with them.

We will share how our ministry went in the past week and talk about any plans we need to make for the upcoming week.

We will then spend time in prayer for our lost friends and our plans for the week.

WORLD || 10 minutes

The World time will help us learn a little more about the world in which we live. Each week, the "Know God's World" section will provide a few facts about the world. In the "Share Helpful Resources" section, a different team member will take responsibility for learning about the resource of the week and then share about it with the team. We will choose one person to research and share for the next week. We will finish the World time in prayer for the nations.

WORD || 20 minutes

The Word time gives our community an opportunity to discuss the "Daily Quiet Times" and the "Learning Questions" from *Spiritual Multiplication in the Real World* from the previous week. This time will also be used to review the "Key Verse."

GAME PLAN

This is a convenient list of everything we need to do before next week's Team Meeting. We will use this to keep track of assignments and set goals.

LEARNING QUESTIONS

Each week, we will be assigned one or two chapters from the book *Spiritual Multiplication in the Real World*. There are questions in this workbook that will help guide our learning and discussion. We will complete our reading and answer the questions before we show up to Team Meeting each week.

DAILY QUIET TIMES

Each week, we will have a set of Daily Quiet Times to guide our three hours of time with God. These readings go along with the topics of *Spiritual Multiplication in the Real World*. Each of us should read the verses in context to get the full picture of what is being said.

KEY VERSE

These are important verses that come from our weekly readings. Each week, we will memorize the assigned verse and be prepared to recite it at the Team Meeting.

WEEK ONE

Introduction Meeting

WELCOME II 15 MINUTES

Have everyone introduce themselves by answering these questions:

   What is your name?

   Why do you want to be in a disciple-making team?

Take some time to familiarize yourselves with this entire workbook.

Read through together and discuss the Introduction (p. 1-6).

Sign the Covenant (p. 2).

WITNESS II 10 MINUTES

What did you see God do this week?

WORSHIP II 10 MINUTES

Thank God together in prayer for what he did last week.

Use an iPod, guitar, etc. and sing a few songs together.

WORKS II 25 MINUTES

FISHING CHART

Turn to the FISHing chart (p. 118). Take a few minutes to write down the names of your lost friends and relatives who live in the same town as you. If you don't have ten, then make a plan to meet new people this week.

DEBRIEF

As a group, write the names of your lost friends somewhere that's visible for everyone to see. After all the names are written, circle around and pray for your friends.

TOOLS

The leader should introduce "My Story: Interest-Creating Testimony" (p. 120) and then demonstrate how to share it by telling their own using the outline. You will be working on your story throughout this week and will practice sharing it at Team Meeting next week.

ACTIVITY

Turn to the Game Plan on the next page and fill in your goals for this week.

GAME PLAN FOR NEXT WEEK

3 HOURS *with Jesus*

Daily Quiet Times
Memorize Key Verse: Mark 4:20

2 HOURS *with lost people*

If your FISHing chart is not full, meet new people
I will meet _____ new people this week

1 HOUR *with each other in prayer*

This week I will pray with _____

LEARNING ASSIGNMENT

Complete "My Story: Creating Interest Testimony" worksheet (p. 120)
Read *Spiritual Multiplication in the Real World* (Ch. 1-2) and answer the
Learning Questions

WEEK TWO

Chapter 1: Stars and Sand
Chapter 2: Maybe Someone Else

KEY VERSE

Mark 4:20
But those that were sown on the good soil are the ones who hear the word and accept it and bear fruit, thirtyfold and sixtyfold and a hundredfold.

PIRITUAL MULTIPLICATION IN THE REAL WORLD

WORD

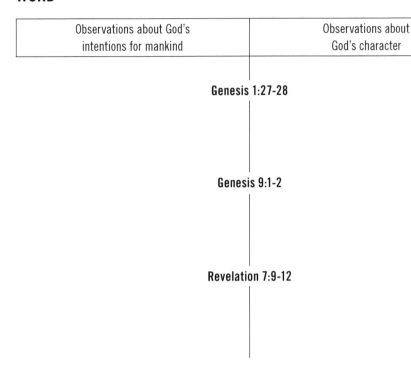

Observations about God's intentions for mankind	Observations about God's character
Genesis 1:27-28	
Genesis 9:1-2	
Revelation 7:9-12	

WORSHIP

Praise God for what you saw about him in the Word today.

Today I thank God for...

I will worship God by obeying in the following ways this week:

Today I will trust God for...

▷ Learn this week's Key Verse.

WORD

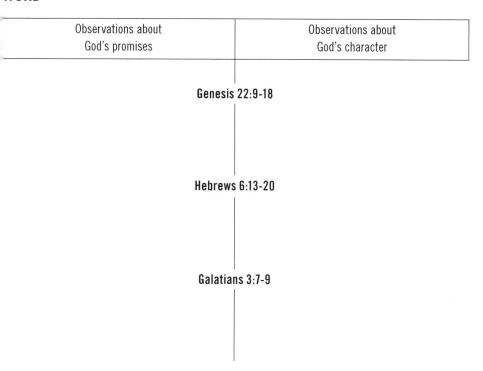

Observations about God's promises	Observations about God's character
Genesis 22:9-18	
Hebrews 6:13-20	
Galatians 3:7-9	

How do the promises made to Abraham apply to you?

Describe the encouragement you find in these verses.

Write a specific life goal related to multiplication that you would like to trust God to accomplish through your life.

WORSHIP

Praise God for what you saw about him in the Word today.

Today I thank God for...

I will worship God by obeying in the following ways this week:

Today I will trust God for...

Review this week's Key Verse.

WORD

Principles of spiritual multiplication observed	Observations about God's character

2 Timothy 1

WORSHIP

Praise God for what you saw about him in the Word today.

Today I thank God for...

I will worship God by obeying in the following ways this week:

Today I will trust God for...

▷ Review this week's Key Verse.

WORD

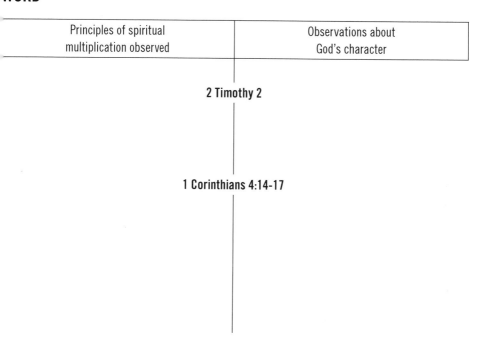

Principles of spiritual multiplication observed	Observations about God's character

2 Timothy 2

1 Corinthians 4:14-17

WORSHIP

Praise God for what you saw about him in the Word today.

Today I thank God for...

I will worship God by obeying in the following ways this week:

Today I will trust God for...

Review this week's Key Verse.

WORD

Principles of spiritual multiplication observed	Observations about God's character
2 Timothy 3 (especially verses 10-11)	

WORSHIP

Praise God for what you saw about him in the Word today.

Today I thank God for...

I will worship God by obeying in the following ways this week:

Today I will trust God for...

▷ Review this week's Key Verse.

WORD

Principles of spiritual multiplication observed	Observations about God's character

2 Timothy 4

WORSHIP

Praise God for what you saw about him in the Word today.

Today I thank God for...

I will worship God by obeying in the following ways this week:

Today I will trust God for...

Review this week's Key Verse.

SUMMARY AND REFLECTION DAY

After looking over this week's quiet times, summarize what God has been teaching you.

What specific action will you take to apply what you have learned?

Did you really meet with Jesus this week, or did you just go through the motions?

WORSHIP

Praise God for what you saw about him in the Word this week.

Today I thank God for...

I will worship God by obeying in the following ways this week:

Today I will trust God for...

▷ Write out this week's Key Verse below:

SPIRITUAL MULTIPLICATION IN THE REAL WORLD (Chapters 1-2)

1. How did you answer the four questions from page 1:

- Is it hard for you to believe God wants to multiply your life and make your spiritual descendants as numerous as the stars in the sky and the sand on the seashore? Why or why not?

- What are you specifically asking God to do through your life?

- How many men or women are you asking God to equip as multiplying disciples through you?

- How many nations are you asking God to impact through you? Describe how reading about the doctrine of multiplication impacted you.

Spiritual multiplication is God's plan for reaching the world, and he has no Plan B. In light of this, how should we respond to failure in our efforts to multiply?

What lies do you think Satan wants Christians to believe about spiritual multiplication in the real world? What lies have you believed?

In light of God's awesome power, is there something big you want to trust God to do through your life this year?

What is your number one takeaway from reading Chapters 1-2?

WELCOME II 15 MINUTES

Have each person answer the question:

Who has had the greatest impact on your spiritual life?

Split into pairs and share your Interest-Creating Testimony with a partner, giving each other feedback on how to make your story more clear or interest-creating.

WITNESS II 10 MINUTES

What did you see God do this week?

WORSHIP II 10 MINUTES

Thank God together in prayer for what he did last week.

Use an iPod, guitar, etc. and sing a few songs together.

WORKS II 25 MINUTES

FISHING CHART

Turn to the FISHing chart (p. 118) and write names of your lost friends on it.

The ideal people to have on your FISHing Chart are people:

Whom you will be able to see repeatedly

Who would be open to your influence

Discuss as a team where and how each of you can meet people who fulfill the two criteria above.

It's okay if you can't fill the chart this week. You will be working as a team to fill in new people in the coming weeks.

Turn to p. 121 and read about asking questions, then decide how many people you will share your story with this week. Write it in the Game Plan.

DEBRIEF

Write down the names of the new lost friends you met this week. When all the names have been written, put the list in the middle of the group and pray for those listed. Do not hurry this prayer time. It is the life blood of your ministry as a team and should therefore be central in each of your meetings.

ACTIVITY

Turn to the Game Plan on the next page and fill in your goals for this week.

WORLD II 10 MINUTES

KNOW GOD'S WORLD: Missionaries

Ninety-nine percent of believers live and work among the 60 percent of the world's population that already has the gospel.

Only 10 percent of missionaries work among the 40 percent of the world's population that is considered unreached.

Three out of every five non-Christians live beyond the reach of same-culture evangelism. Someone will have to intentionally cross cultural or language barriers to reach them.[1]

SHARE HELPFUL RESOURCES

Assign next week's resource: Global Prayer Digest (globalprayerdigest.org)

PRAY FOR THE NATIONS

WORD II 10 MINUTES

Share Mark 4:20 with a partner.

Discuss the major learning points and application steps from your Daily Quiet Times (Day 7).

Discuss your answers to the Learning Questions for *Spiritual Multiplication in the Real World* (Ch. 1-2).

Close with prayer.

GAME PLAN FOR NEXT WEEK

3 HOURS *with Jesus*

Daily Quiet Times
Memorize Key Verse: Acts 2:46-47

2 HOURS *with lost people*

If your FISHing chart is not full, meet new people.
I will meet _____ new people this week

Share your story
I will share my story with _____ people this week

My ministry partner this week will be _____

1 HOUR *with each other in prayer*

This week I will pray with _____

LEARNING ASSIGNMENT

Read *Spiritual Multiplication in the Real World* (Ch. 3-4) and answer the Learning Questions

WEEK THREE

Chapter 3: Trouble in Multiplication Paradise

Chapter 4: Soil

KEY VERSE

Acts 2:46-47
And day by day, attending the temple together and breaking bread in their homes, they received their food with glad and generous hearts, praising God and having favor with all the people. And the Lord added to their number day by day those who were being saved.

PIRITUAL MULTIPLICATION IN THE REAL WORLD

WORD

Foundations for ministry that were laid	Observations about God's will and his ways

Acts 1

WORSHIP

Praise God for what you saw about him in the Word today.

Today I thank God for...

I will worship God by obeying in the following ways this week:

Today I will trust God for...

▷ Learn this week's Key Verse.

WORD

Observations about living in community and disciple-making as a team	Ways in which God displayed his goodness
Acts 2	

WORSHIP

Praise God for what you saw about him in the Word today.

Today I thank God for...

I will worship God by obeying in the following ways this week:

Today I will trust God for...

Review this week's Key Verse.

WORD

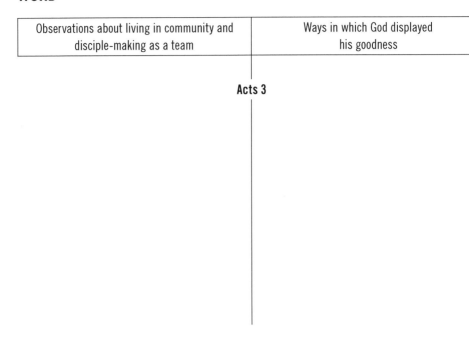

Observations about living in community and disciple-making as a team	Ways in which God displayed his goodness

Acts 3

WORSHIP

Praise God for what you saw about him in the Word today.

Today I thank God for...

I will worship God by obeying in the following ways this week:

Today I will trust God for...

▷ Review this week's Key Verse.

WORD

Observations about living in community and teamwork	Observations about Jesus

Acts 4

WORSHIP

Praise God for what you saw about him in the Word today.

Today I thank God for...

I will worship God by obeying in the following ways this week:

Today I will trust God for...

Review this week's Key Verse.

WORD

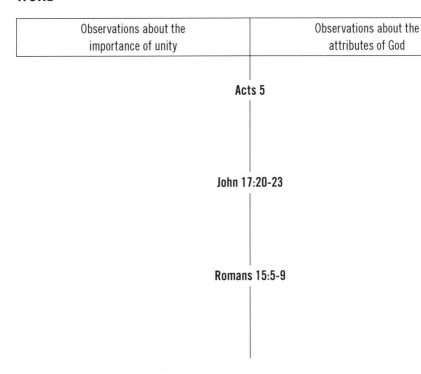

Observations about the importance of unity	Observations about the attributes of God
Acts 5	
John 17:20-23	
Romans 15:5-9	

WORSHIP

Praise God for what you saw about him in the Word today.

Today I thank God for...

I will worship God by obeying in the following ways this week:

Today I will trust God for...

▷ Review this week's Key Verse.

WORD

Benefits of teamwork	Observations about God's grace in suffering

Acts 6

WORSHIP

Praise God for what you saw about him in the Word today.

Today I thank God for...

I will worship God by obeying in the following ways this week:

Today I will trust God for...

Review this week's Key Verse.

SUMMARY AND REFLECTION DAY

After looking over this week's quiet times, summarize what God has been teaching you.

What specific action will you take to apply what you have learned?

Did you really meet with Jesus this week, or did you just go through the motions?

WORSHIP

Praise God for what you saw about him in the Word this week.

Today I thank God for...

I will worship God by obeying in the following ways this week:

Today I will trust God for...

▷ Write out this week's Key Verse below:

SPIRITUAL MULTIPLICATION IN THE REAL WORLD (Chapters 3-4)

1. Have you ever tried to multiply spiritually? If so, how did it go?

2. Respond to the statement, "If you're not fishing, you're not following." Why do you agree or disagree?

3. Describe the type of group that you will need to be a part of if you are going to multiply your life consistently over the coming years.

4. What thoughts come to mind when you read about the impact your life could have if you too applied the biblical principles practiced by highly effective disciple-makers?

How do you think American individualism has affected the way we think about disciple-making?

What specific action step do you need to take to apply what you learned in your reading this week?

WELCOME II 15 MINUTES

Have each person answer the question:

> What is one book (besides the Bible) that has impacted your spiritual life?

Split into pairs and share your story with a new partner, giving each other feedback on how to make your story more clear or interest-creating.

WITNESS II 10 MINUTES

What did you see God do this week?

WORSHIP II 10 MINUTES

Thank God together in prayer for what he did last week.

Make a list of the names of God and praise him for his attributes.

WORKS II 25 MINUTES

FISHING CHART

Update your FISHing chart with any new people you met this week or steps you took in the FISHing process.

DEBRIEF

Add your team's new friends to your list. Put the list in the middle of the group and pray over your friends.

ACTIVITY

Turn to p. 122 and read about a Matthew Party. Then spend some time as a group planning one together.

Turn to the Game Plan on the next page and fill in your goals for this week.

WORLD II 10 MINUTES

KNOW GOD'S WORLD: Money

Of foreign mission funding, 87 percent is used for work among those already Christian. Twelve percent of funding is spent for work among those who are already evangelized but non-Christians. One percent is used for work among unevangelized and unreached people.[1] According to the National Retail Federation, in 2011, Americans spent the same amount on Halloween costumes (for their pets!).

Do you know of ways that you can ensure that a more significant portion of your giving goes to reaching those who have never heard of Jesus?

SHARE HELPFUL RESOURCES

Report on this week's resource: Global Prayer Digest (globalprayerdigest. org)

Assign next week's resource: Finishing the Task (finishingthetask.com)

PRAY FOR THE NATIONS

WORD II 20 MINUTES

Share Acts 2:46-47 with a partner.

Discuss the major learning points and application steps from your Daily Quiet Times (Day 7).

Discuss your answers to the Learning Questions for *Spiritual Multiplication in the Real World* (Ch. 3-4).

Close with prayer.

GAME PLAN FOR NEXT WEEK

3 HOURS *with Jesus*

Daily Quiet Times
Memorize Key Verse: Hebrews 10:24-25

2 HOURS *with lost people*

If your FISHing chart is not full, meet new people and use the Interest-Creating Questions.
I will meet _____ new people this week

Share your story
I will share my story with _____ people this week

My ministry partner this week will be _____

Plan a Matthew Party

1 HOUR *with each other in prayer*

This week I will pray with _____

LEARNING ASSIGNMENT

Read *Spiritual Multiplication in the Real World* (Ch. 5) and answer the Learning Questions

WEEK FOUR

Chapter 5: Essential Elements

KEY VERSE

Hebrews 10:24-25
And let us consider how to stir up one another to love and good works, not neglecting to meet together, as is the habit of some, but encouraging one another, and all the more as you see the Day drawing near.

WORD

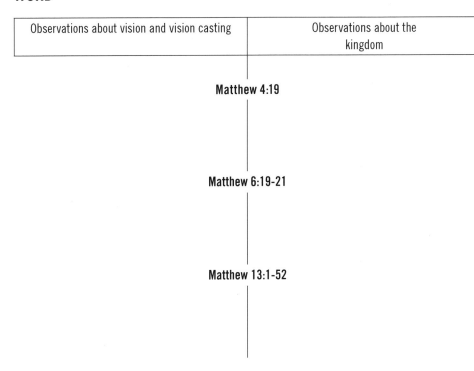

Observations about vision and vision casting	Observations about the kingdom

Matthew 4:19

Matthew 6:19-21

Matthew 13:1-52

What do you need to do to put yourself in a situation where you are consistently challenged with an eternal and multiplying vision?

Whom do you need to encourage this week, and how will you cast vision with them?

WORSHIP

Praise God for what you saw about him in the Word today.

Today I thank God for...

I will worship God by obeying in the following ways this week:

Today I will trust God for...

▷ Learn this week's Key Verse.

WORD

What do you observe regarding the role of modeling in spiritual multiplication?

John 13:15

2 Thessalonians 3:9

Titus 2:7-8

1 Corinthians 4:16-17

1 Corinthians 11:1

What attribute of Christ do you most admire and want to model for those you disciple?

WORSHIP

Praise God for what you saw about him in the Word today.

Today I thank God for...

I will worship God by obeying in the following ways this week:

Today I will trust God for...

Review this week's Key Verse.

WORD

Observations regarding training and coaching	Observations about Jesus

Matthew 17

WORSHIP

Praise God for what you saw about him in the Word today.

Today I thank God for...

I will worship God by obeying in the following ways this week:

Today I will trust God for...

▷ Review this week's Key Verse.

WORD

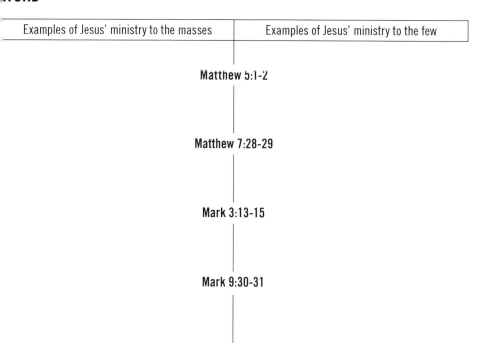

Examples of Jesus' ministry to the masses	Examples of Jesus' ministry to the few

Matthew 5:1-2

Matthew 7:28-29

Mark 3:13-15

Mark 9:30-31

Why is ministry to both the masses and the few important?

What relationship do you see between ministry to the masses and ministry to the few in spiritual multiplication?

Do you think you need to increase your ministry to the masses or the few? What steps will you take?

How do you see Jesus' love in his ministry to the masses and the few?

WORSHIP

Praise God for what you saw about him in the Word today.

Today I thank God for...

I will worship God by obeying in the following ways this week:

Today I will trust God for...

Review this week's Key Verse.

WORD

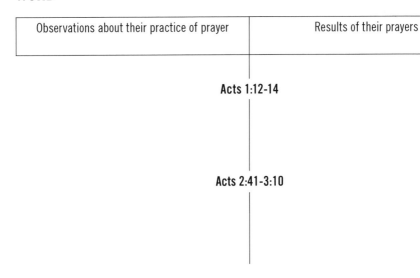

Observations about their practice of prayer	Results of their prayers
Acts 1:12-14	
Acts 2:41-3:10	

What steps will you take to devote yourself to prayer?

WORSHIP

Praise God for what you saw about him in the Word today.

Today I thank God for...

I will worship God by obeying in the following ways this week:

Today I will trust God for...

▷ Review this week's Key Verse.

WORD

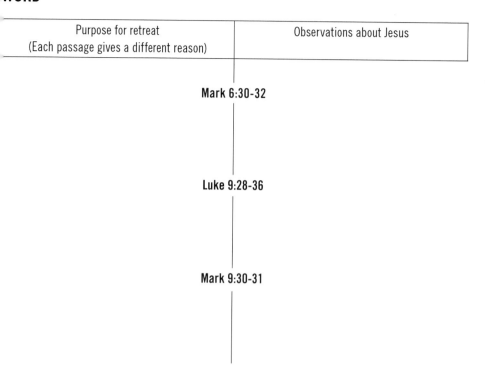

Purpose for retreat (Each passage gives a different reason)	Observations about Jesus
Mark 6:30-32	
Luke 9:28-36	
Mark 9:30-31	

Do you need to plan a retreat soon? For what purpose?

WORSHIP

Praise God for what you saw about him in the Word today.

Today I thank God for...

I will worship God by obeying in the following ways this week:

Today I will trust God for...

Review this week's Key Verse.

SUMMARY AND REFLECTION DAY

After looking over this week's quiet times, summarize what God has been teaching you.

What specific action will you take to apply what you have learned?

Did you really meet with Jesus this week, or did you just go through the motions?

WORSHIP

Praise God for what you saw about him in the Word this week.

Today I thank God for...

I will worship God by obeying in the following ways this week:

Today I will trust God for...

▷ Write out this week's Key Verse below:

SPIRITUAL MULTIPLICATION IN THE REAL WORLD (Chapter 5)

1. What are the differences between a church that is designed to grow in attendance and one that is designed to equip and help its members multiply their lives?

2. Why is it so important to be part of a church that possesses the seven essential elements of a disciple-making movement?

What do you think the author is saying are the main differences between a standard small group and a disciple-making team?

What is your major takeaway from this chapter? How will you apply what you learned?

WELCOME II 15 MINUTES

Have each person answer the question:

> Who do you know that most models the vision of spiritual multiplication? Why did you pick this person?

Split into pairs and share your story with a new partner, giving each other feedback on how to make your story more clear or interest-creating.

WITNESS II 10 MINUTES

What did you see God do this week?

WORSHIP II 10 MINUTES

Thank God together in prayer for what he did last week.

Read Psalm 136 responsively: one person reads the first half of a verse, and everyone reads the second half together.

WORKS II 25 MINUTES

FISHING CHART

Update your FISHing chart with any new people you met this week or steps you took in the FISHing process.

DEBRIEF

Add your team's new friends to your list. Put the list in the middle of the group and pray over your friends.

ACTIVITY

Turn to the Game Plan on the next page and fill in your goals for this week.

WORLD II 10 MINUTES

KNOW GOD'S WORLD: 10/40 Window

Eighty-six percent of all unreached people groups lie within the region called the 10/40 window, which is between 10 and 40 degrees north latitude, from the west coast of Africa to the east coast of Asia.[2]

These people are not "more lost" than your unsaved neighbor or family member, but they are "unreached" in the sense that they have not had the opportunity to hear the Gospel.[4]

SHARE HELPFUL RESOURCES

Report on this week's resource: Finishing the Task (finishingthetask.com)

Assign next week's resource: Open Doors (opendoors.org)

PRAY FOR THE NATIONS

WORD II 20 MINUTES

Share Hebrews 10:24-25 with a partner.

Discuss the major learning points and application steps from your Daily Quiet Times (Day 7).

Discuss your answers to the Learning Questions for *Spiritual Multiplication in the Real World* (Ch. 5).

Close with prayer.

GAME PLAN FOR NEXT WEEK

3 HOURS *with Jesus*

Daily Quiet Times
Memorize Key Verse: John 13:35

2 HOURS *with lost people*

If your FISHing chart is not full, meet new people and use the Interest-Creating Questions.
I will meet _____ new people this week

Share your story
I will share my story with _____ people this week

My ministry partner this week will be _____

1 HOUR *with each other in prayer*

This week I will pray with _____

LEARNING ASSIGNMENT

Read *Spiritual Multiplication in the Real World* (Ch. 6) and answer the Learning Questions

WEEK FIVE

Chapter 6: Gone Fishing

KEY VERSE

John 13:35
By this all people will know that you are my disciples, if you have love for one another.

WORD

Observations about evangelism	How Jesus created interest

John 4:1-45

What do you observe about Jesus in this passage that impresses you?

WORSHIP

Praise God for what you saw about him in the Word today.

Today I thank God for...

I will worship God by obeying in the following ways this week:

Today I will trust God for...

▷ Learn this week's Key Verse.

WORD

In Luke 10:1, how did Jesus send his disciples out to do evangelism?

What advantages do you see in approaching evangelism as a team rather than as individuals?

John 13:34-35

1 Corinthians 14:24-25

In light of these verses, what changes will you make to how you evangelize?

WORSHIP

Praise God for what you saw about him in the Word today.

Today I thank God for...

I will worship God by obeying in the following ways this week:

Today I will trust God for...

Review this week's Key Verse.

WORD

Observations about evangelism	Observations about God

Acts 17:16-31

Finding out about people

Interesting people in the gospel

Sharing the good news

Helping people make a decision

In light of these verses, what changes will you make to how you evangelize?

WORSHIP

Praise God for what you saw about him in the Word today.

Today I thank God for...

I will worship God by obeying in the following ways this week:

Today I will trust God for...

▷ Review this week's Key Verse.

WORD

Observations about evangelism	Observations about God

1 Corinthians 3:1-23

WORSHIP

Praise God for what you saw about him in the Word today.

Today I thank God for...

I will worship God by obeying in the following ways this week:

Today I will trust God for...

Review this week's Key Verse.

WORD

Observations about evangelism	Observations about Jesus

Matthew 11:25-30

Observations about creating interest

Observations about calling people to a decision

WORSHIP

Praise God for what you saw about him in the Word today.

Today I thank God for...

I will worship God by obeying in the following ways this week:

Today I will trust God for...

▷ Review this week's Key Verse.

WORD

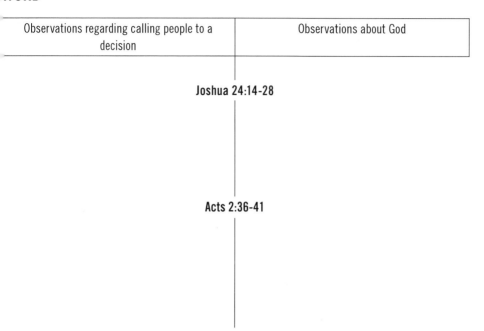

Observations regarding calling people to a decision	Observations about God
Joshua 24:14-28	
Acts 2:36-41	

Is there someone you need to invite to follow Jesus this week?

WORSHIP

Praise God for what you saw about him in the Word today.

Today I thank God for...

I will worship God by obeying in the following ways this week:

Today I will trust God for...

Review this week's Key Verse.

SUMMARY AND REFLECTION DAY

After looking over this week's quiet times, summarize what God has been teaching you.

What specific action will you take to apply what you have learned?

Did you really meet with Jesus this week, or did you just go through the motions?

WORSHIP

Praise God for what you saw about him in the Word this week.

Today I thank God for...

I will worship God by obeying in the following ways this week:

Today I will trust God for...

▷ Write out this week's Key Verse below:

SPIRITUAL MULTIPLICATION IN THE REAL WORLD (Chapter 6)

1. What was something new you learned from your reading this week?

2. Evaluate yourself in the following areas and share your answers with the group.
(1 = Weakness, 3 = Average, 5 = Strength)

____ Finding new people with whom to share the gospel

____ Finding out about people's lives (asking good questions)

____ Creating interest

____ Sharing the Gospel

____ Helping people make a decision and deal with barriers

What steps will you take to grow in your weak areas?

WELCOME II 15 MINUTES

Have each person answer the question:

> What is the best news you have ever heard (besides the gospel)?

> How long did it take you to start telling others about your good news?

Split into pairs and share your story with a new partner, giving each other feedback on how to make your story more clear or interest-creating.

WITNESS II 10 MINUTES

What did you see God do this week?

WORSHIP II 10 MINUTES

Thank God together in prayer for what he did last week.

Have a time of silence before the Lord to hear his voice and worship. Ask him to bring to mind a verse you could use to worship him or encourage the group. Pray the verse back to the Lord.

WORKS II 25 MINUTES

FISHING CHART

Update your FISHing chart with any new people you met this week or steps you took in the FISHing process.

DEBRIEF

Add your team's new friends to your list. Put the list in the middle of the group and pray over your friends.

ACTIVITY

Turn to the Game Plan on the next page and fill in your goals for this week.

WORLD II 10 MINUTES

KNOW GOD'S WORLD: Tribals

There are 161 million people in 704 tribal people groups.[1]

They have animistic and superstitious beliefs (everything has a spirit, such as water, rocks, trees, animals).

They must be careful not to offend these spirits and must appease them with sacrifices.

They often worship idols and ancestors and visit witch doctors.

SHARE HELPFUL RESOURCES

Report on this week's resource: Open Doors (opendoors.org)

Assign next week's resource: Voice of the Martyrs (persecution.org)

PRAY FOR THE NATIONS

WORD II 20 MINUTES

Share John 13:35 with a partner.

Discuss the major learning points and application steps from your Daily Quiet Times (Day 7).

Discuss your answers to the Learning Questions for *Spiritual Multiplication in the Real World* (Ch. 6).

Close with prayer.

GAME PLAN FOR NEXT WEEK

3 HOURS *with Jesus*

Daily Quiet Times
Memorize Key Verse: 1 Thessalonians 2:7-8

2 HOURS *with lost people*

I will create interest with _____ (person on FISHing chart) by
doing _____ (interest-creating activity).

My ministry partner this week will be _____

1 HOUR *with each other in prayer*

This week I will pray with _____

LEARNING ASSIGNMENT

Read *Spiritual Multiplication in the Real World* (Ch. 7) and answer the
Learning Questions

WEEK SIX

Chapter 7: Parenthood

KEY VERSE

1 Thessalonians 2:7-8
But we were gentle among you, like a nursing mother taking care of her own children. So, being affectionately desirous of you, we were ready to share with you not only the gospel of God but also our own selves, because you had become very dear to us.

WORD

Observations about discipling relationships	Observations about God

1 Thessalonians 1

WORSHIP

Praise God for what you saw about him in the Word today.

Today I thank God for...

I will worship God by obeying in the following ways this week:

Today I will trust God for...

▷ Learn this week's Key Verse.

WORD

Observations about discipling relationships	Observations about God

1 Thessalonians 2

WORSHIP

Praise God for what you saw about him in the Word today.

Today I thank God for...

I will worship God by obeying in the following ways this week:

Today I will trust God for...

Review this week's Key Verse.

WORD

Observations about discipling relationships	Observations about God

1 Thessalonians 3

WORSHIP

Praise God for what you saw about him in the Word today.

Today I thank God for...

I will worship God by obeying in the following ways this week:

Today I will trust God for...

▷ Review this week's Key Verse.

WORD

Observations about discipling relationships	Observations about God

1 Thessalonians 4

WORSHIP

Praise God for what you saw about him in the Word today.

Today I thank God for...

I will worship God by obeying in the following ways this week:

Today I will trust God for...

Review this week's Key Verse.

WORD

Observations about discipling relationships	Observations about God

1 Thessalonians 5

WORSHIP

Praise God for what you saw about him in the Word today.

Today I thank God for...

I will worship God by obeying in the following ways this week:

Today I will trust God for...

▷ Review this week's Key Verse.

WORD

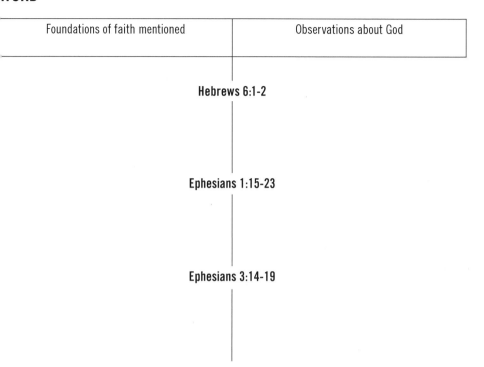

Foundations of faith mentioned	Observations about God

Hebrews 6:1-2

Ephesians 1:15-23

Ephesians 3:14-19

WORSHIP

Praise God for what you saw about him in the Word today.

Today I thank God for...

I will worship God by obeying in the following ways this week:

Today I will trust God for...

Review this week's Key Verse.

SUMMARY AND REFLECTION DAY

After looking over this week's quiet times, summarize what God has been teaching you.

What specific action will you take to apply what you have learned?

Did you really meet with Jesus this week, or did you just go through the motions?

WORSHIP

Praise God for what you saw about him in the Word this week.

Today I thank God for...

I will worship God by obeying in the following ways this week:

Today I will trust God for...

▷ Write out this week's Key Verse below:

SPIRITUAL MULTIPLICATION IN THE REAL WORLD (Chapter 7)

. What are the needs of a new disciple?

. What are some of the key things a disciple-maker can do to help a new believer become established in the faith?

. What are some traps to avoid when establishing new believers?

Why does the author discourage discipling someone one-on-one?

What specific application steps do you believe you need to take in light of what you read in this chapter?

With whom will you share what you learned in this chapter?

WELCOME II 15 MINUTES

Share a story of an answered prayer.

WITNESS II 10 MINUTES

What did you see God do this week?

WORSHIP II 10 MINUTES

Thank God together in prayer for what he did last week.

Use an iPod, guitar, etc. and sing a few songs together.

WORKS II 25 MINUTES

FISHING CHART

Update your FISHing chart with any new people you met this week or steps you took in the FISHing process.

DEBRIEF

Add your team's new friends to your list. Put the list in the middle of the group and pray over your friends.

TOOLS

The leader should introduce "The Bridge Illustration" (p. 123) and then demonstrate how to share it.

Pair up and practice The Bridge with another teammate, giving each other feedback.

ACTIVITY

Plan another Matthew Party as a group.

Turn to the Game Plan on the next page and fill in your goals for this week.

WORLD II 10 MINUTES

KNOW GOD'S WORLD: Hindus

There are 860 million people in 1,843 Hindu people groups.[1]

They believe in millions of gods.

They worship idols of clay, stone, or pictures by giving them food, flowers, and money.

They believe they are caught in a cycle of birth-death-rebirth called reincarnation.

SHARE HELPFUL RESOURCES

Report on this week's resource:
Voice of the Martyrs (persecution.org)

Assign next week's resource:
Perspectives on the World Christian Movement (perspectives.org)

PRAY FOR THE NATIONS

WORD II 20 MINUTES

Share 1 Thessalonians 2:7-8 with a partner.

Discuss the major learning points and application steps from your Daily Quiet Times (Day 7).

Discuss your answers to the Learning Questions for *Spiritual Multiplication in the Real World* (Ch. 7).

Close with prayer.

GAME PLAN FOR NEXT WEEK

3 HOURS *with Jesus*

Daily Quiet Times
Memorize Key Verse: Ephesians 4:11-12

2 HOURS *with lost people*

Plan a Matthew Party

Share The Bridge
I will share The Bridge with _____ people this week

My ministry partner this week will be _____

1 HOUR *with each other in prayer*

This week I will pray with _____

LEARNING ASSIGNMENT

Read *Spiritual Multiplication in the Real World* (Ch. 8) and answer the
Learning Questions

WEEK SEVEN

Chapter 8: Learning to Fly

KEY VERSE

Ephesians 4:11-12
And he gave the apostles, the prophets, the evangelists, the shepherds and teachers, to equip the saints for the work of ministry, for building up the body of Christ,

WORD

Disciple-making and equipping observations	Observations about God

1 Timothy 1

WORSHIP

Praise God for what you saw about him in the Word today.

Today I thank God for...

I will worship God by obeying in the following ways this week:

Today I will trust God for...

▷ Learn this week's Key Verse.

WORD

Disciple-making and equipping observations	Observations about God

1 Timothy 2

WORSHIP

Praise God for what you saw about him in the Word today.

Today I thank God for...

I will worship God by obeying in the following ways this week:

Today I will trust God for...

Review this week's Key Verse.

WORD

Disciple-making and equipping observations	Observations about God

1 Timothy 3

WORSHIP

Praise God for what you saw about him in the Word today.

Today I thank God for...

I will worship God by obeying in the following ways this week:

Today I will trust God for...

▷ Review this week's Key Verse.

WORD

Disciple-making and equipping observations	Observations about God

1 Timothy 4

WORSHIP

Praise God for what you saw about him in the Word today.

Today I thank God for...

I will worship God by obeying in the following ways this week:

Today I will trust God for...

Review this week's Key Verse.

WORD

Disciple-making and equipping observations	Observations about God

1 Timothy 5

WORSHIP

Praise God for what you saw about him in the Word today.

Today I thank God for...

I will worship God by obeying in the following ways this week:

Today I will trust God for...

▷ Review this week's Key Verse.

WORD

Disciple-making and equipping observations	Observations about God

1 Timothy 6

WORSHIP

Praise God for what you saw about him in the Word today.

Today I thank God for...

I will worship God by obeying in the following ways this week:

Today I will trust God for...

Review this week's Key Verse.

SUMMARY AND REFLECTION DAY

After looking over this week's quiet times, summarize what God has been teaching you.

What specific action will you take to apply what you have learned?

Did you really meet with Jesus this week, or did you just go through the motions?

WORSHIP

Praise God for what you saw about him in the Word this week.

Today I thank God for...

I will worship God by obeying in the following ways this week:

Today I will trust God for...

▷ Write out this week's Key Verse below:

SPIRITUAL MULTIPLICATION IN THE REAL WORLD (Chapter 8)

. What is the best example of equipping you have ever seen?

. What areas of your life are not good models for others?

. Summarize what you believe were the author's major points regarding selection.

. Do you agree or disagree with the author's emphasis on character development in the equipping stage of ministry? Why?

What is still unclear to you about the equipping phase of ministry?

What specific application steps do you believe you need to take in light of what you read in this chapter?

With whom will you share what you learned in this chapter?

WELCOME II 15 MINUTES

What have you found to be most helpful in spending quality time alone fellowshipping with God?

WITNESS II 10 MINUTES

What did you see God do this week?

WORSHIP II 10 MINUTES

Thank God together in prayer for what he did last week.

As a group, write down a list of as many of God's attributes as you can.

WORKS II 25 MINUTES

FISHING CHART
Update your FISHing chart with any new people you met this week or steps you took in the FISHing process.

DEBRIEF
Add your team's new friends to your list. Put the list in the middle of the group and pray over your friends.

TOOLS
Pair up and practice The Bridge with another teammate, giving each other feedback.

ACTIVITY
Turn to the Game Plan on the next page and fill in your goals for this week.

WORLD II 10 MINUTES

KNOW GOD'S WORLD: Unreligious

There are 121 million people in 15 Unreligious people groups.[1]

They are mostly atheistic, with some remnants of ancestor worship or Buddhist beliefs.

Many have Communist governments that tell people there is no God.

The majority lives in the country of China.

SHARE HELPFUL RESOURCES
Report on this week's resource: Perspectives on the World Christian Movement (perspectives.org)

Assign next week's resource: Launch Global (launchglobal.org)

PRAY FOR THE NATIONS

WORD II 20 MINUTES

Share Ephesians 4:11-12 with a partner.

Discuss the major learning points and application steps from your Daily Quiet Times (Day 7).

Discuss your answers to the Learning Questions for Spiritual Multiplication in the Real World (Ch. 8).

Close with prayer.

GAME PLAN FOR NEXT WEEK

3 HOURS *with Jesus*

Daily Quiet Times
Memorize Key Verse: Matthew 9:37-38

2 HOURS *with lost people*

Share The Bridge
I will share The Bridge with _____ people this week

My ministry partner this week will be _____

1 HOUR *with each other in prayer*

This week I will pray with _____

LEARNING ASSIGNMENT

Read *Spiritual Multiplication in the Real World* (Ch. 9) and answer the
Learning Questions

WEEK EIGHT

hapter 9: The Lost Aspect of Disciple-Making

KEY VERSE

Matthew 9:37-38
Then he said to his disciples, "The harvest is plentiful, but the laborers are few; therefore pray earnestly to the Lord of the harvest to send out laborers into his harvest."

WORD

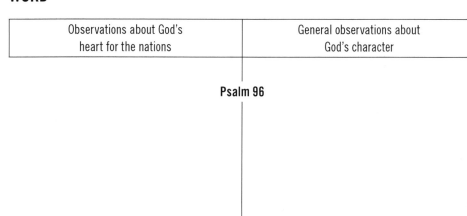

Observations about God's heart for the nations	General observations about God's character

Psalm 96

WORSHIP

Praise God for what you saw about him in the Word today.

Today I thank God for...

I will worship God by obeying in the following ways this week:

Today I will trust God for...

▷ Learn this week's Key Verse.

WORD

Observations about God's heart for the nations	General observations about God's character
Matthew 9:35-38	

WORSHIP

Praise God for what you saw about him in the Word today.

Today I thank God for...

I will worship God by obeying in the following ways this week:

Today I will trust God for...

Review this week's Key Verse.

WORD

Observations about God's heart for the nations	General observations about God's character

Romans 10:5-17

WORSHIP

Praise God for what you saw about him in the Word today.

Today I thank God for...

I will worship God by obeying in the following ways this week:

Today I will trust God for...

▷ Review this week's Key Verse.

WORD

Observations about God's heart for the nations	General observations about God's character

Romans 15

WORSHIP

Praise God for what you saw about him in the Word today.

Today I thank God for...

I will worship God by obeying in the following ways this week:

Today I will trust God for...

Review this week's Key Verse.

WORD

Observations about God's heart for the nations	General observations about God's character

Revelation 5

WORSHIP

Praise God for what you saw about him in the Word today.

Today I thank God for...

I will worship God by obeying in the following ways this week:

Today I will trust God for...

▷ Review this week's Key Verse.

WORD

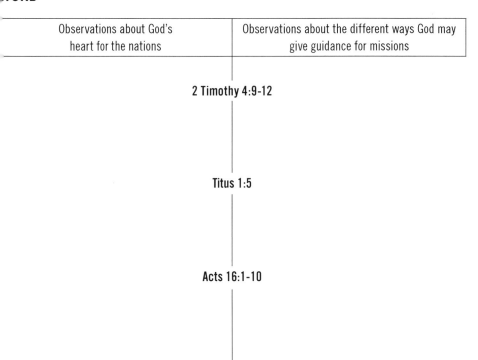

Observations about God's heart for the nations	Observations about the different ways God may give guidance for missions

2 Timothy 4:9-12

Titus 1:5

Acts 16:1-10

WORSHIP

Praise God for what you saw about him in the Word today.

Today I thank God for...

I will worship God by obeying in the following ways this week:

Today I will trust God for...

Review this week's Key Verse.

SUMMARY AND REFLECTION DAY

After looking over this week's quiet times, summarize what God has been teaching you.

What specific action will you take to apply what you have learned?

Did you really meet with Jesus this week, or did you just go through the motions?

WORSHIP

Praise God for what you saw about him in the Word this week.

Today I thank God for...

I will worship God by obeying in the following ways this week:

Today I will trust God for...

▷ Write out this week's Key Verse below:

SPIRITUAL MULTIPLICATION IN THE REAL WORLD (Chapter 9)

. What do you think has caused such a great imbalance of laborers in the world today?

. Why do you think most disciple-makers and church leaders are not more actively mobilizing their people to the unreached?

. What new things did you learn from this chapter?

Is there anything in your life that is keeping you from successfully mobilizing laborers?

What action step will you take this week to apply what you learned about exporting?

WELCOME II 15 MINUTES

Were you more of an obedient or disobedient child growing up?

Why do you think you were the way you were?

WITNESS II 10 MINUTES

What did you see God do this week?

WORSHIP II 10 MINUTES

Thank God together in prayer for what he did last week.

Use an iPod, guitar, etc. and sing a few songs together.

WORKS II 25 MINUTES

FISHING CHART
Update your FISHing chart with any new people you met this week or steps you took in the FISHing process.

DEBRIEF
Add your team's new friends to your list. Put the list in the middle of the group and pray over your friends.

TOOLS
The leader should introduce "God's Heart for the Nations" (p. 127) and then demonstrate how to share it.

Pair up and practice "God's Heart for the Nations" with another teammate, giving each other feedback.

ACTIVITY
Turn to the Game Plan on the next page and fill in your goals for this week.

WORLD II 10 MINUTES

KNOW GOD'S WORLD: Muslim

There are 1.3 billion people in 1,344 Muslim people groups.[1]

They believe in one God, named Allah, and that Mohammad was his final prophet.

They believe if the good deeds done in life outweigh the bad deeds, Muslims go to Paradise when they die.

They respect Jesus as a good prophet but do not believe he is God.

SHARE HELPFUL RESOURCES
Report on this week's resource: Launch Global (launchglobal.org)

Assign next week's resource: Joshua Project (joshuaproject.net)

PRAY FOR THE NATIONS

WORD II 20 MINUTES

Share Matthew 9:37-38 with a partner.

Discuss the major learning points and application steps from your Daily Quiet Times (Day 7).

Discuss your answers to the Learning Questions for *Spiritual Multiplication in the Real World* (Ch. 9).

Close with prayer.

GAME PLAN FOR NEXT WEEK

3 HOURS *with Jesus*

Daily Quiet Times
Memorize Key Verse: 2 Corinthians 3:5-6

2 HOURS *with lost people*

Share God's Heart for the Nations
I will share God's Heart for the Nations with _____ people this week

My ministry partner this week will be _____

1 HOUR *with each other in prayer*

This week I will pray with _____

LEARNING ASSIGNMENT

Read *Spiritual Multiplication in the Real World* (Ch. 10) and answer the
Learning Questions

WEEK NINE

Chapter 10: You Can!

KEY VERSE

2 Corinthians 3:5-6
Not that we are sufficient in ourselves to claim anything as coming from us, but our sufficiency is from God, who has made us sufficient to be ministers of a new covenant, not of the letter but of the Spirit. For the letter kills, but the Spirit gives life.

WORD: 1 Timothy 1:18, 4:11-16; 2 Timothy 1:6-7

In what ways was Paul empowering Timothy with his words in 1 Timothy 4:11-16?

To whom should you speak encouraging and empowering truth today?

WORSHIP

Praise God for what you saw about him in the Word today.

Today I thank God for...

I will worship God by obeying in the following ways this week:

Today I will trust God for...

▷ Learn this week's Key Verse.

WORD: Matthew 10:19-20, Acts 1:8

How did Jesus empower his disciples in these verses?

To whom should you speak encouraging and empowering truth today?

WORSHIP

Praise God for what you saw about him in the Word today.

Today I thank God for...

I will worship God by obeying in the following ways this week:

Today I will trust God for...

Review this week's Key Verse.

WORD: Matthew 17:19-21, 21:21

How was Jesus empowering his disciples in these verses?

To whom should you speak encouraging and empowering truth today?

WORSHIP

Praise God for what you saw about him in the Word today.

Today I thank God for...

I will worship God by obeying in the following ways this week:

Today I will trust God for...

▷ Review this week's Key Verse.

WORD: Luke 10:19, Matthew 28:20

What can you learn about empowering from what Jesus said in these verses?

How will you apply these truths to your life and ministry?

WORSHIP

Praise God for what you saw about him in the Word today.

Today I thank God for...

I will worship God by obeying in the following ways this week:

Today I will trust God for...

Review this week's Key Verse.

WORD: 2 Corinthians 3:5-6

In light of these verses, how should you think about your ability to minister to others?

How will you act upon this truth?

WORSHIP

Praise God for what you saw about him in the Word today.

Today I thank God for...

I will worship God by obeying in the following ways this week:

Today I will trust God for...

▷ Review this week's Key Verse.

WORD: Philippians 4:13, 2 Corinthians 12:9-10

How should these verses influence your thinking about what you attempt in ministry?

How will you act upon these truths?

WORSHIP

Praise God for what you saw about him in the Word today.

Today I thank God for...

I will worship God by obeying in the following ways this week:

Today I will trust God for...

Review this week's Key Verse.

SUMMARY AND REFLECTION DAY

After looking over this week's quiet times, summarize what God has been teaching you

What specific action will you take to apply what you have learned?

Did you really meet with Jesus this week, or did you just go through the motions?

WORSHIP

Praise God for what you saw about him in the Word this week.

Today I thank God for...

I will worship God by obeying in the following ways this week:

Today I will trust God for...

▷ Write out this week's Key Verse below:

SPIRITUAL MULTIPLICATION IN THE REAL WORLD (Chapter 10)

. Many believers feel ill-equipped to disciple others because they think discipling others is something only a highly knowledgeable and wise person can do. The author presents a different view than this. Explain what you believe the author's view is and your reaction to it.

. Review the lies that Satan tells people mentioned in Chapter 10. What are the lies you find yourself believing most frequently?

If you knew for sure that God's power was upon you and that anything you attempted for him would succeed, what do you believe he would want you to attempt?

WELCOME II 15 MINUTES

Who do you know who is most committed to fulfilling the Great Commission, and what is it that you see in his or her life that makes you select this person?

WITNESS II 10 MINUTES

What did you see God do this week?

WORSHIP II 10 MINUTES

Thank God together in prayer for what he did last week.

Take turns reading a few verses of Psalm 145, stopping to praise God for who he is and what he does.

WORKS II 25 MINUTES

FISHING CHART

Update your FISHing chart with any new people you met this week or steps you took in the FISHing process.

DEBRIEF

Add your team's new friends to your list. Put the list in the middle of the group and pray over your friends.

TOOLS

The leader should introduce "Sharing the Vision of Multiplication" (p. 125) and then demonstrate how to share it.

Pair up and practice "Sharing the Vision of Multiplication" with another teammate, giving each other feedback.

ACTIVITY

Turn to the Game Plan on the next page and fill in your goals for this week.

WORLD II 10 MINUTES

KNOW GOD'S WORLD: Buddhists

There are 275 million people in 227 Buddhist people groups.[1]

They believe that suffering is caused by desire.

To end suffering, they must rid themselves of desire through meditation and multiple reincarnations.

The ultimate goal is to reach Nirvana, where suffering ends and the self ceases to exist.

SHARE HELPFUL RESOURCES

Report on this week's resource: Joshua Project (joshuaproject.net)

Assign next week's resource: The Traveling Team (thetravelingteam. org)

PRAY FOR THE NATIONS

WORD II 20 MINUTES

Share 2 Corinthians 3:5-6 with a partner.

Discuss the major learning points and application steps from your Daily Quiet Times (Day 7).

Discuss your answers to the Learning Questions for *Spiritual Multiplication in the Real World* (Ch. 10).

Close with prayer.

GAME PLAN FOR NEXT WEEK

3 HOURS *with Jesus*

Daily Quiet Times
Memorize Key Verse: Galatians 6:9

2 HOURS *with lost people*

This week, the evangelistic activity I will do is: _____

I will do an evangelistic activity with _____ people this week

Share the Vision for Spiritual Multiplication

I will share the Vision for Spiritual Multiplication with _____ people this week

My ministry partner this week will be _____

1 HOUR *with each other in prayer*

This week I will pray with _____

LEARNING ASSIGNMENT

Read *Spiritual Multiplication in the Real World* (Ch. 11) and answer the
Learning Questions

WEEK TEN

hapter 11: From Vision to Reality

KEY VERSE

Galatians 6:9
And let us not grow weary of doing good, for in due season we will reap, if we do not give up.

WORD

Requirements for Multiplication	Observations about God

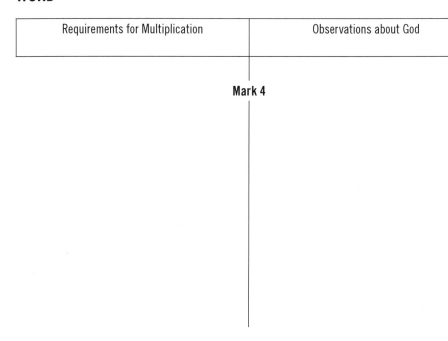

Mark 4

What does this passage teach will be required to see your vision of spiritual multiplication become a reality?

WORSHIP

Praise God for what you saw about him in the Word today.

Today I thank God for...

I will worship God by obeying in the following ways this week:

Today I will trust God for...

▷ Learn this week's Key Verse.

WORD

Requirements for Multiplication	Observations about God

John 15

What does this passage teach will be required to see your vision of spiritual multiplication become a reality?

WORSHIP

Praise God for what you saw about him in the Word today.

Today I thank God for...

I will worship God by obeying in the following ways this week:

Today I will trust God for...

Review this week's Key Verse.

WORD: Matthew 6:24, 2 Timothy 2:4, John 12:20-26

What do these passages teach will be required to see your vision of spiritual multiplication become a reality?

What do you need to do to apply what is taught in these verses?

WORSHIP

Praise God for what you saw about him in the Word today.

Today I thank God for...

I will worship God by obeying in the following ways this week:

Today I will trust God for...

▷ Review this week's Key Verse.

WORD: Hebrews 4:14-16

What does this passage teach will be required to see your vision of spiritual multiplication become a reality?

What do you need to do to apply what is taught in these verses?

WORSHIP

Praise God for what you saw about him in the Word today.

Today I thank God for...

I will worship God by obeying in the following ways this week:

Today I will trust God for...

Review this week's Key Verse.

WORD: Revelation 2:1-7

What does this passage teach will be required to see your vision of spiritual multiplication become a reality?

What do you need to do to apply what is taught in these verses?

WORSHIP

Praise God for what you saw about him in the Word today.

Today I thank God for...

I will worship God by obeying in the following ways this week:

Today I will trust God for...

▷ Review this week's Key Verse.

WORD: **Galatians 6:9, 1 Corinthians 15:58**

What do these passages teach will be required to see your vision of spiritual multiplication become a reality?

What do you need to do to apply what is taught in these verses?

WORSHIP

Praise God for what you saw about him in the Word today.

Today I thank God for...

I will worship God by obeying in the following ways this week:

Today I will trust God for...

Review this week's Key Verse.

SUMMARY AND REFLECTION DAY

After looking over this week's quiet times, summarize what God has been teaching you.

What specific action will you take to apply what you have learned?

Did you really meet with Jesus this week, or did you just go through the motions?

WORSHIP

Praise God for what you saw about him in the Word this week.

Today I thank God for...

I will worship God by obeying in the following ways this week:

Today I will trust God for...

▷ Write out this week's Key Verse below:

SPIRITUAL MULTIPLICATION IN THE REAL WORLD (Chapter 11)

. After reading about the direct relationship between one's time alone with God and one's fruitfulness in ministry, do you need to make any changes in your devotional practices? If so, what are they?

. What "other visions" or "cares of the world" do you need to deal with if you are going to multiply your life?

Which of the "First Steps" do you need to take?

What are some of the things in your plan that you are trusting God to do through your life?

Whom are you going to ask to team up with you in the mission of disciple-making?

If you gave up on disciple-making one day in the future, what do you think would be the reason?

The author described our mission in this way, "As part of a disciple-making team, go and multiply disciple-making teams in all nations." Do you think explaining our mission in this way is helpful? Why or why not?

WELCOME II 15 MINUTES

Share how this group has helped you over the last nine weeks.

WITNESS II 10 MINUTES

What did you see God do this week?

WORSHIP II 10 MINUTES

Thank God together in prayer for what he did last week.

Use an iPod, guitar, etc. and sing a few songs together.

WORKS II 25 MINUTES

FISHING CHART

Update your FISHing chart with any new people you met this week or steps you took in the FISHing process.

DEBRIEF

Add your team's new friends to your list. Spend an extended time praying for all of your friends on this list.

ACTIVITY

Discuss and fill out "My Disciple-Making Plan" on p. 129.

Discuss the future of your team.

WORLD II 10 MINUTES

KNOW GOD'S WORLD: Internationals

There are over 680,000 international students who study and live in the United States every year.[5]

Sixty percent of international students come from the 10/40 Window.

Forty percent of the world's 220 Heads of State once studied in the US.

Eighty percent of these students will return to their countries having never been invited to an American home.[4]

SHARE HELPFUL RESOURCES
Report on this week's resource: The Traveling Team (thetravelingteam.org)

PRAY FOR THE NATIONS

WORD II 20 MINUTES

Share Galatians 6:9 with a partner.

Discuss the major learning points and application steps from your Daily Quiet Times (Day 7).

Discuss your answers to the Learning Questions for *Spiritual Multiplication in the Real World* (Ch. 11).

Close with prayer.

APPENDIX

FISHING CHART

MY STORY: CREATING INTEREST TESTIMONY

FIND: QUESTIONS

GLOSSARY

BRIDGE ILLUSTRATION

SHARING THE VISION FOR MULTIPLICATION

GOD'S HEART FOR THE NATIONS

MY DISCIPLE-MAKING PLAN

FISHING CHART

#	FIND				INTEREST					SHARE				HELP	
	Name	Interests	Felt Needs	Attitude Toward Jesus	Testimony	Answered Prayer Stories	Community	Prayer for their needs	Jesus Story	Discovery Bible Study	Gospel Presentation	Something to Read	Ask for a Decision	Deal with Barriers
1														
2														
3														
4														
5														
6														
7														
8														
9														
10														

#	FIND				INTEREST				SHARE				HELP	
	Name	Interests	Felt Needs	Attitude Toward Jesus	Testimony	Answered Prayer Stories	Community	Prayer for their needs	Jesus Story	Discovery Bible Study	Gospel Presentation	Something to Read	Ask for a Decision	Deal with Barriers
1														
2														
3														
4														
5														
6														
7														
8														
9														
10														

I first sensed my need for Jesus when…

What made me most interested in Jesus was…

I finally decided to trust Jesus and follow him when I realized that…

Since I entered into a relationship with Jesus, I have changed

From: To:

From:

To:

Jesus helps me in my daily life by…

I have seen God answer my prayers in some pretty cool ways, like the time…

_____ have you ever considered learning about how to follow Jesus?

When meeting new people, the easiest way to begin getting to know them is by asking questions. It is usually best to start by asking biographical questions before asking more personal questions about their interests and needs. Take a minute to read over the following example questions. Then take turns practicing asking questions and moving the conversation from biographical to interests to needs.

. Biographical questions:

> Where are you from?

> Where do you live now?

> What do you do?

> Tell me about your family.

Interests questions: (Hopefully, these questions will help you find some ways you can spend time together in the future.)

> Do you have any hobbies or favorite sports?

> What is your favorite thing to do in your free time?

Needs questions:

> I try to pray for the needs of people I meet. Is there anything specific I can pray for you?

THE LEGEND OF BIG BLUE

In 2007, a dedicated group of believers in Iowa began to meet as a missional community. A cornerstone of their weekly meetings was a time of prayer for the lost. Names of lost friends were written on a leftover piece of blue flooring material, which was then laid in the middle of the room to be prayed over. Each week, as members recalled people they had met, new names were added to the list. A time of intense prayer would follow as disciples got on their knees to pray over "Big Blue." As these groups multiplied and spread to other states, so did the inclusion of Big Blue. Get a blue piece of fabric or poster board and join the movement!

MATTHEW PARTY

A Matthew Party is a get-together planned for people who need to meet Jesus. We get the name from Matthew, the tax collector, who held a reception in his home for people to come meet Jesus. One of the goals of this event is to allow our lost friends to experience the difference Christ makes in a community of believers. It is important that we aren't outnumbered, as seeing Christ-centered community in action is the goal behind this gathering. We want them to see the love we have for one another. A Matthew Party can be a dinner, a game night, bowling, ice skating, some sort of cultural activity, etc. The important thing is allowing our lost friends to spend time with a group of believers.

LUKE 5:29-32 (ESV)

And Levi [Matthew] made him [Jesus] a great feast in his house, and there was a large company of tax collectors and others reclining at table with them. And the Pharisees and their scribes grumbled at his disciples, saying, "Why do you eat and drink with tax collectors and sinners?"

And Jesus answered them, "Those who are well have no need of a physician, but those who are sick. I have not come to call the righteous but sinners to repentance."

JOHN 13:35

By this all people will know that you are my disciples, if you have love for one another.

If you need a video demonstration of The Bridge, several good versions can be found online.

YOUR POTENTIAL IMPACT

If you only discipled two people per year and taught them to teach others to multiply each year, you could multiply over 3 _Billion_ disciples in just twenty years.

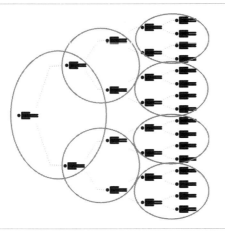

☐ Draw circles around groups of disciples and discuss the importance of multiplying not only disciples, but disciple-making teams.

WHAT ACTION WILL YOU TAKE?

☐ I will seek out someone to disciple me.

☐ I will seek out people to disciple.

WHAT PAUL DID

"And what you have heard from me in the presence of many witnesses entrust to faithful men who will be able to teach others also."

2 Timothy 2:2

Paul — Silas — Titus

Timothy — _faithful_

faithful men — _faithful_ — _others_

others — _others_

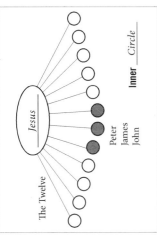

The Twelve

Jesus

Peter
James
John

Inner _Circle_

WHAT JESUS COMMANDED

"Therefore go and _make_ _disciples_ of _all_ _nations_, baptizing them in the name of the Father and of the Son and of the Holy Spirit."

Matthew 28:19

WHAT JESUS PROMISED

"Others, like seed sown on good soil, hear the word, accept it, and produce a crop—some _30_, some _60_, some _100_ times what was sown."

Mark 4:20

WHAT JESUS DID

The Twelve

Peter
James
John

Inner ____

WHAT JESUS COMMANDED

"Therefore go and ____ of ____ the name of the Father and of the Son and of the Holy Spirit."

Matthew 28:19

WHAT JESUS PROMISED

"Others, like seed sown on good soil, hear the word, accept it, and produce a crop—some ____, some ____, some ____ times what was sown."

Mark 4:20

WHAT PAUL DID

"And what you have heard from me in the presence of many witnesses entrust to faithful men who will be able to teach others also."

2 Timothy 2:2

Paul

Silas

Titus

YOUR POTENTIAL IMPACT

If you only discipled two people per year and taught them to teach others to multiply each year, you could multiply over 3 ____ disciples in just twenty years.

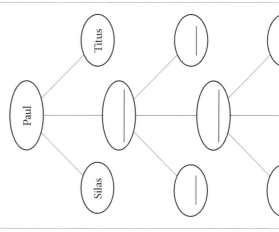

☐ Draw circles around groups of disciples and discuss the importance of multiplying not only disciples, but disciple-making teams.

WHAT ACTION WILL YOU TAKE?

☐ I will seek out someone to disciple me.

☐ I will seek out people to disciple.

1 THE GRAND NARRATIVE

1. Commission to multiply God's image bearers in all the earth: **Genesis 1:28**

2. Image marred: **Genesis 3:15**

3. People Groups Formed: **Genesis 11:8**

4. God's plan to bless all nations through Abraham's Children: **Genesis 12:2-3**

5. Example of an Old Testament imperative to preach to the nations: **1 Chronicles 16:24**

6. All believers are children of Abraham and have the same blessings and responsibilities: **Galatians 3:7-9**

7. The gospel of the kingdom and the demonstration of its power went to the Jews first: **Matthew 10:6-8**

8. The blessing is supposed to spread to all nations: **Acts 1:8**

9. Jesus has commanded all of his followers to spread his kingdom to the nations (ethne): **Matthew 28:18-20**

10. We should make the unreached our ambition: **Romans 15:20**

11. Jesus ransomed all nations: **Revelation 5:9**

12. All nations will be in heaven: **Revelation 7:9**

2 THE GREAT IMBALANCE

60%
Reached

_40_ **%**
Unreached

The average American spends **$20 per week** on coffee.

The average American Christian gives _1.5 cents_ to the unreached each week.

3 YOUR PART

WHAT DO YOU THINK IS YOUR MOST STRATEGIC ROLE?

1. Go
2. Give
3. Pray
4. _Welcome_
5. _Mobilize_
6. _Other:_

WHAT DO YOU THINK IS YOUR MOST STRATEGIC LOCATION?

. . . . **Sending**	. . . . **Reached**
Unengaged	_Unreached_

WHAT DO YOU THINK IS YOUR MOST STRATEGIC NEXT STEP?

1 — THE GRAND NARRATIVE

1. Commission to multiply God's image bearers in all the earth: **Genesis 1:28**

2. Image marred: **Genesis 3:15**

3. People Groups Formed: **Genesis 11:8**

4. God's plan to bless all nations through Abraham's Children: **Genesis 12:2-3**

5. Example of an Old Testament imperative to preach to the nations: **1 Chronicles 16:24**

6. All believers are children of Abraham and have the same blessings and responsibilities: **Galatians 3:7-9**

7. The gospel of the kingdom and the demonstration of its power went to the Jews first: **Matthew 10:6-8**

8. The blessing is supposed to spread to all nations: **Acts 1:8**

9. Jesus has commanded all of his followers to spread his kingdom to the nations (ethne): **Matthew 28:18-20**

10. We should make the unreached our ambition: **Romans 15:20**

11. Jesus ransomed all nations: **Revelation 5:9**

12. All nations will be in heaven: **Revelation 7:9**

2 — THE GREAT IMBALANCE

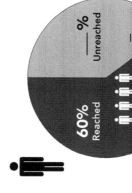

60% Reached

_____ **%** Unreached —

The average American spends **$20 per week** on coffee.

The average American Christian gives _____ to the unreached each week.

3 — YOUR PART

WHAT DO YOU THINK IS YOUR MOST STRATEGIC ROLE?

1. Go
2. Give
3. Pray
4. _____
5. _____
6. _____

WHAT DO YOU THINK IS YOUR MOST STRATEGIC LOCATION?

Sending	**Reached**

WHAT DO YOU THINK IS YOUR MOST STRATEGIC NEXT STEP?

VISION: I would like to see the following vision become a reality:

TRUSTING GOD: I am trusting God to do the following:

Before I die:

In the next three years:

In the next twelve months:

In the next three months:

I am claiming the following promises from God's Word:

SHARING THE VISION: I will ask the following people to join me in the vision and to speak into it:

PIN IT UP: I will put a visual reminder in the following places:

FOUNDATIONS:
MISSIONAL COMMUNITY GUIDEBOOK

AN ESTABLISHING TOOL

This resource is designed to lead new believers into missional community an outreach while establishing them in the foundations of the faith. Together, discipl learn how to grow spiritually and bear fruit as obedient followers of Chris Foundations is a proven tool to practically build up your disciples in the basics of Christ-centered life while they reach out to others as a community. It will solidi their faith through the study of the following lessons:

Week 1: My Story

Week 2: The Gospel

Week 3: Assurance of Salvation

Week 4: Following Christ as Lord

Week 5: Living in Grace

Week 6: Purpose in Life

Week 7: Quiet Time

Week 8: The Word

Week 9: Prayer

Week 10: Life in the Spirit

Week 11: Perseverance in Suffering

ENDNOTES

The Task Remaining by Ralph D. Winter and Bruce A. Koch, *Perspectives on the World Christian Movement, Reader.* 4th ed. William Carey Library, 2009, p.531-546. *www.missionbooks.org*

Joshua Project, *www.joshuaproject.org*

The Coming Revolution: Because Status Quo Missions Won't Finish the Job by Mark R. Baxter, Tate Publishing, 2007, p.12.

The Traveling Team, *www.thetravelingteam.org*

Statistics from The Institute of International Education, Inc. *www.iie.org*

Made in the USA
Coppell, TX
18 January 2023

11334326R00077